SPORT FIRST AID WORKBOOK

Fifth Edition

American Sport Education Program

HUMAN KINETICS

Sport First Aid Workbook, Fifth Edition

ISBN-10: 1-4504-6891-8 (print)
ISBN-13: 978-1-4504-6891-6 (print)

Printed in the United States of America   10

The paper in this book is certified under a sustainable forestry program.

Human Kinetics
P.O. Box 5076
Champaign, IL 61825-5076
Website: www.HumanKinetics.com

In the United States, email info@hkusa.com or call 800-747-4457.
In Canada, email info@hkcanada.com.
In the United Kingdom/Europe, email hk@hkeurope.com.

For information about Human Kinetics' coverage in other areas of the world,
please visit our website: **www.HumanKinetics.com**

E6158

Contents

Preface

Welcome to the *Sport First Aid* classroom course! The goal of this course is two-fold: to inform you on the best practices to help your athletes avoid athletic injuries and to help you become an effective first responder when one of your athletes gets injured or becomes ill. The classroom course and test preparation activities are designed to help you learn what steps you should take to become confident in responding to your athletes' injuries and illnesses.

The *Sport First Aid Workbook* is your guide and resource for completing the two activities mentioned previously: classroom course and test preparation activities. You'll use it during the classroom course as your instructor leads you through activities, videos, and discussions. All of the resources you need for the classroom course are in the workbook, and plenty of space has been left for you to write notes at the end of each unit.

After you've completed the classroom course, you'll use the test preparation assignments to prepare for the Sport First Aid test. These assignments include reading the course text, *Sport First Aid*, and working through the units in the *Sport First Aid Online Component*. Attending the classroom course, reading the text, and completing the online component should prepare you for the Sport First Aid test. Just as important, these activities should enhance your ability to be an effective sport first aider for the athletes you coach.

ASEP hopes that you find the course and supporting resources valuable in contributing to your efforts to be a successful coach. We wish you the best of success in providing meaningful sport experiences for your athletes.

Introduction to Sport First Aid

(23 minutes)

PURPOSE: To introduce you to the Sport First Aid course, including the course purpose, learning objectives, agenda, and resources.

LEARNING OBJECTIVES

In this unit, coaches will learn about

- the course resources;
- the purpose, learning objectives, and agenda for the Sport First Aid course; and
- the procedures for completing the test preparation and test phases of the course.

Unit Overview

Topic	Activities	Time (minutes)
A. Welcome and Introductions	Course welcome Course resources	10
B. Overview of the Sport First Aid Course	Purpose, objectives, and agenda for the course	3
C. Completing the Course	Section introduction Procedures for completing the test preparation and test phases of the course Housekeeping details Unit summary and the learning environment	10

UNIT CONTENT

A Welcome and Introductions (10 minutes)

- Be prepared to introduce yourself by giving your
  - name,
  - present position,
  - sports coached, and
  - length of career.

Course Packages

- The course text, *Sport First Aid*, or, alternatively, a key code letter (included in the test package) with the key code to access the *Sport First Aid* e-book
- *Sport First Aid Workbook*
- A Sport First Aid classroom test package that includes the following:
  - Sport First Aid classroom test
  - ASEP Test Answer Form A to record test answers
  - Sport First Aid test instructions
  - Preaddressed ASEP mailing envelope for the coach to mail the completed ASEP Test Answer Form A
  - Cardboard insert to ensure that the test form is not damaged in the mail
  - Key code letter with the key code to access the *Sport First Aid Online Component*

Sport Fist Aid Workbook

- Each unit includes the following:
  - Unit's purpose, learning objectives, overview, and sections (A, B, and so forth)
  - Summary of the unit introduction
  - For every activity: an introduction; instructions that describe the resources to use, steps to complete, and the outcome of your work; and activity worksheets for you to write on to complete the activity
  - In the workbook: space for you to write notes at the end of each unit. This space is denoted with the word "notes" in parentheses.

Sport First Aid

- The first few chapters of the *Sport First Aid* book contain general information for you as a coach and as a first responder in injury and illness situations.
- Chapters 4 and 5 cover the emergency action steps and physical assessment, which we'll be spending a lot of time on during this course.
- Chapter 6 describes how to move an injured or ill athlete.
- Chapters 7 through 15 list injuries and illnesses that you might encounter as a coach, with corresponding symptoms and signs for easier recognition and appropriate first aid steps for you to take.

Test Options

- You can complete the course test using a paper–pencil form, or you can complete it online.
- Everything you'll need to do for either test is described in the Sport First Aid test instructions booklet.

Test Information

- If you take the paper–pencil test, you'll enter this information on the answer form.
- If you take the online test, you'll enter this information online.

REFER to the Test Information form on page 72 in the *Sport First Aid Workbook*, and **ENTER** the information described by the instructor.

B Overview of the Sport First Aid Course (3 minutes)

The purpose of the Sport First Aid course is to help you learn the skills you need to be a competent first responder to players' injuries and illnesses. This course has been designed to help you

- develop a basic knowledge of sport injuries and illnesses,
- recognize signs and symptoms of common sport injuries and illnesses,
- administer appropriate sport first aid, and
- learn to use the *Sport First Aid* book as a reference tool.

Sport First Aid Classroom Course Agenda

Unit number	Unit title	Time (minutes)
1	Introduction to Sport First Aid	23
2	Your Role on the Athletic Health Care Team	15
3	Types of Injuries	20
4	Emergency Action Steps	50
	BREAK (IN TWO-DAY FORMAT, MAY STOP FIRST DAY HERE.)	**10**
5	Physical Assessment and Providing Immediate First Aid	60
6	Moving Injured or Sick Athletes	10
7	Head, Spine, and Nerve Injuries	20
8	Musculoskeletal Injuries	35
9	Sport First Aid Wrap-Up	16
	TOTAL TIME:	**4 HOURS, 15 MINUTES** (not including breaks)

C Completing the Course (10 minutes)

Course Topics

- For the first couple of hours today, we will discuss your role on the athletic health care team, types of injuries and illnesses, and how to conduct emergency action steps.
- Then we'll take a 10-minute break.
- We'll finish up the day by learning how to conduct a physical assessment, control bleeding, minimize shock, apply splints and compression wraps, move an injured or ill athlete, provide first aid care for head and spine injuries, and handle musculoskeletal injuries.
- Before you head home, we'll wrap things up and discuss how you can use the book, the workbook, and the online component to prepare for the Sport First Aid classroom test.

Test Preparation and Test Procedures

- Over the next several weeks, you need to complete the other phases of Sport First Aid—the test preparation phase of the course and the Sport First Aid test.
  - The steps for completing the test are described in the Sport First Aid test instructions included in your test package.
  - You should plan to complete these activities by _____.
  - If you do not successfully pass your Sport First Aid test within one year of the last date of your course (today), you will have to take the entire course over again and pay all of the course fees again.

- Before you take the test, you should read *Sport First Aid* and complete the related activities included in the online component.
  - Instructions for accessing the *Sport First Aid Online Component* are included on the key code letter in your course package.
  - All of the activities we complete today and all of the activities you complete during the test preparation will help you become effective coaches and will help you pass the test. However, do not fail to carefully read every chapter in *Sport First Aid* because all of the test questions are based on content in the book.

- The last thing you'll do to complete the course is to complete the course test.
  - You can complete the paper–pencil test, or you can complete the test online.
  - The instructions and forms you'll need to complete the course test are included in this Sport First Aid classroom test package.
  - The package contains the Sport First Aid test instructions, which provide a detailed description of what you need to do to complete the course test. After reading *Sport First Aid* and completing the related online activities, you really have only three things to do:
    1. Decide whether you'll complete the paper–pencil test or the online test.
    2. Complete the test.
    3. Get your test scored.

- At the end of the course today, we'll discuss things you should consider in deciding whether to take the paper–pencil test or the online test.
- Whichever test you take, it's important to remember the following:
  - The course test is open book. You can refer to *Sport First Aid* and any other course materials while you complete the test.
  - You should complete the test individually unless the instructor tells you otherwise.
  - If you do not pass the test the first time, you can take it again. The procedures for taking a retest are described in the test instructions.
  - If you complete your first test paper–pencil, you must complete retests in the paper–pencil format. If you complete your first test online, you must complete retests in the online format.

The Learning Environment

- Feel free to ask questions at any time. There are no dumb questions. Be assertive about what you need to understand sport first aid better.
- Use the workbook in whatever way makes it easier for you to learn. Take notes, make check marks, underline important things—do whatever you need to do to make it a worthwhile resource.
- Relax. Enjoy yourself. Be open. Participate. We're all here to learn together.

(Notes)

Your Role on the Athletic Health Care Team

(15 minutes)

PURPOSE: To introduce you to your role in working on the athletic health care team and teach you how to prepare a sport first aid game plan.

LEARNING OBJECTIVES

In this unit, you will learn

- about the athletic health care team and your role on it and
- how to develop a sport first aid game plan.

Unit Overview

Topic	Activities	Time (minutes)
A. Unit Introduction	Hear about the unit's purpose, objectives, and agenda.	1
B. Coach's Role on the Athletic Health Care Team and How to Develop a Sport First Aid Game Plan	Watch a DVD segment, "Your Role on the Athletic Health Care Team."	5
C. Evaluating Your Sport First Aid Game Plan	Fill out Chapter 2 Replay on page 9 in the workbook.	8
D. Unit Summary	Review key unit points.	1

UNIT CONTENT

A Unit Introduction (1 minute)

- Your role on the athletic health care team and how to prepare a sport first aid game plan
- What you need to do to complete a sport first aid game plan for your particular situation

B Coach's Role on the Athletic Health Care Team and How to Develop a Sport First Aid Game Plan (5 minutes)

On the DVD Segment, "Your Role on the Athletic Health Care Team"

- Legal definitions of your role as a coach
- Parental expectations
- Other members of the athletic health care team
- Playing it safe with return to play, including the importance of treatment and rehabilitation
- How to develop a sport first aid game plan

C Evaluating Your Sport First Aid Game Plan (8 minutes)

Activity 2.1 Evaluating Your Sport First Aid Game Plan

Introduction

You heard on the DVD segment that to be prepared for emergencies, you need to develop a sport first aid game plan. This involves collecting health records of your athletes, creating a weather emergency plan, preparing a medical emergency plan, and so forth.

- For the next few minutes, you'll evaluate what you need to do in your particular coaching situation to complete your sport first aid game plan.
- When you complete the self-study portion of this course, you'll actually complete your own sport first aid game plan.

Resources

Chapter 2 Replay from the *Sport First Aid* book

- ☐ Do you regularly study sports medicine literature and attend sports medicine seminars? (pp. 13-14)
- ☐ Are you currently certified in CPR? (p. 14)
- ☐ Have all of your athletes filled out an informed consent form for emergency medical treatment, a health history form, and an emergency information card? (p. 14)
- ☐ Have you prepared and implemented a weather emergency plan? (pp. 15-17)
- ☐ Do you regularly inspect the condition of playing areas and equipment? (pp. 17-20)
- ☐ Do you find and repair any defects in playing equipment before the start of each season? (pp. 17-20)
- ☐ Do you have a well-stocked first aid kit? (pp. 17, 20)
- ☐ Do you require athletes to undergo extensive physical examinations and preseason screening to pinpoint any potential health or fitness problems? (p. 21)
- ☐ Do you have a preseason conditioning plan, and do you incorporate warm-up and cool-down exercises into every practice and competition to help prevent injuries? (pp. 21-22)
- ☐ Do you enforce policies that require athletes to wear protective equipment and refrain from physical horseplay? (pp. 22-25)
- ☐ Do you teach athletes correct sport skill techniques and repeatedly warn them against techniques that are potentially dangerous? (p. 23)
- ☐ Do you provide sound nutritional guidance, sufficient hydration, and nutritional eating opportunities? (pp. 23-25)
- ☐ Have you developed an emergency plan, including who is responsible for what duties, how a duty should be carried out, when certain actions should be taken, and what paperwork needs to be completed? (pp. 25-27)

Instructions

1. Work in pairs.
2. Talk through the checklist together.
3. Check off the items that you've already accomplished in your particular coaching situation and note the steps that you need to complete in the margins of your workbook.

4. Complete the checklist for your situation only, but discuss each item with your partner. You may gain insights from each other about how to efficiently complete certain parts of the sport first aid game plan.

5. You probably won't get through the entire checklist in the time allotted, and that is all right. Complete as much of the checklist as you can now, and then you can finish it on your own later.

6. Take 7 minutes to complete your work.

Activity Outcome

When you're done, you should have completed as much of the checklist as possible. The items that you have already completed in your coaching situation should have a check mark next to them, and you should have a good sense of which steps you still need to take care of.

D Unit Summary (1 minute)

- Along with many other legal duties, you have a legal obligation to provide emergency medical assistance.

- Parents expect you to provide a safe environment for their children. They expect you to have some knowledge of sport first aid and to know where to refer them for more information.

- You should develop good working relationships with other members of the athletic health care team and support their decisions regarding treatment and rehabilitation.

- Players who are injured or sick can return to play only after all symptoms and signs have subsided or after examination and release by a physician.

- A sport first aid game plan includes gathering health records for each athlete, developing a weather emergency plan, checking facilities for hazards, checking equipment for proper fit and usage, stocking a first aid kit, arranging for preseason physicals and fitness screenings, incorporating conditioning into your program, and developing a medical emergency plan.

- Use the forms provided in chapter 2 of *Sport First Aid* to guide you in preparing for emergencies.

(Notes)

Types of Injuries

(20 minutes)

PURPOSE: To help you learn how to recognize the main types of acute and chronic injuries.

LEARNING OBJECTIVES

In this unit, you will learn

- how most injuries occur,
- what distinguishes acute and chronic injuries, and
- how to recognize the main types of acute and chronic injuries.

Unit Overview

Topic	Activities	Time (minutes)
A. Unit Introduction	Hear about the unit's purpose, objectives, and agenda.	1
B. Types of Injuries and How They Occur	Fill out a table while watching the DVD segment, "Types of Injuries and How They Occur."	9
C. Injury Causes	In teams, complete mechanisms (injury causes) columns in a table. Points will be awarded for correct answers.	9
D. Unit Summary	Review key unit points.	1

UNIT CONTENT

A Unit Introduction (1 minute)

- Causes of injury
- Acute injuries
- Chronic injuries

B Types of Injuries and How They Occur (9 minutes)

Activity 3.1 Types of Injuries

Introduction

Knowing how an injury occurred and whether it occurred suddenly or over time may help you to correctly identify an injury and respond with appropriate first aid care. In this activity, you'll fill out a table as we watch a DVD segment.

Resources

- The table, Examples of Injuries That Affect Specific Body Tissues. (This table is provided on page 15.)

Instructions

1. Work individually.
2. As you watch the DVD segment, listen for
   a. what types of injuries affect different body tissues and
   b. whether an injury is acute or chronic.
3. Fill in the table as you watch the DVD segment.
   a. In the second column, write the types of injuries that can affect each body tissue. For example, you'll hear on the DVD segment that bones can sustain closed fractures, so you would write *Closed fracture* in the second column.
   b. In the third column,
      - write *Acute* if the injury occurs suddenly and is the result of a specific injury mechanism,
      - write *Chronic* if the injury develops over a period of several weeks and is typically caused by repeated injury, or
      - write *Acute or Chronic* if both could be the case.

Examples of Injuries That Affect Specific Body Tissues

Tissue	Injury	Type of injury
Bone	Closed fracture	Acute
Cartilage		
Ligament		
Muscle		
Tendon		
Bursa		
Skin		
Eye		
Other organs (heart, kidney, and so forth)		

For example, bones can sustain closed fractures. Closed fractures occur suddenly, so you would write *Acute* in the third column. As you can see, the answers for this injury have been provided in the table as an example.

Activity Outcome

When you're done, you should have completed the "Injury" and "Type of injury" columns in the table. We'll review the results after watching the DVD segment.

C Injury Causes (9 minutes)

Activity 3.2 Injury Causes

Introduction

As explained on the DVD segment, injuries are usually caused by one of three mechanisms: compression, tension, or shearing. In this activity, you'll learn what mechanisms often cause which injuries.

Resources

- The table, Injuries and Their Mechanisms. (This table is provided on page 17.)

Instructions

1. Work in teams of four if possible.
2. Work with your team to decide which mechanisms can cause each injury listed in the table.
3. Place an *X* in the column if that mechanism can cause the injury. For instance, if compression can cause a contusion, place an *X* under *Compression* and across from *Contusion.*
4. You may place more than one *X* in a row. That is, some injuries can be caused by several different mechanisms, and you should place an *X* under each of those. Other injuries may be caused by only one mechanism.
5. You will have 6 minutes to complete the table. You'll need to work quickly.
6. At the end, we will award points for correct answers and see which team won the challenge.

Activity Outcome

When you're done, you should have completed the table with *Xs* in the columns that match the injuries with their mechanisms.

Injuries and Their Mechanisms

Acute injuries	Compression	Tension	Shearing
Contusions			
Abrasions			
Lacerations			
Incisions			
Sprains			
Acute strains			
Cartilage tears			
Dislocations and subluxations			
Bone fractures			
Epiphyseal fractures			
Chronic injuries			
Bursitis			
Tendinosis, tenosynovitis, and paratendinitis			
Stress fractures			

D Unit Summary (1 minute)

- Injuries are often caused by one of three mechanisms: compression, tension, or shearing.
- Injuries can be distinguished by the time it takes for them to develop.
  - Acute injuries occur suddenly as a result of a specific injury mechanism.
  - Chronic injuries develop over a period of several weeks and are typically caused by repeated injury.
- Knowing which mechanism caused an injury and knowing whether the injury occurred suddenly or over time may help you to correctly identify an injury and respond with appropriate first aid care.

(Notes)

Unit 3 Activity Outcomes

Examples of Injuries That Affect Specific Body Tissues—Activity 3.1 Outcome

Tissue	Injury	Type of injury
Bone	Closed fracture Open fracture Avulsion fracture Osteoarthritis Stress fracture	Acute Acute Acute or chronic Chronic Chronic
Cartilage	Tear Contusion	Acute or chronic Acute
Ligament	Sprain	Acute
Muscle	Strain	Acute or chronic
Tendon	Strain Tenosynovitis Tendinosis Paratendinitis	Acute Chronic Chronic Chronic
Bursa	Bursitis Contusion	Chronic Acute
Skin	Laceration Incision Abrasion Puncture Avulsion (example: ear lobe)	Acute Acute Acute Acute Acute
Eye	Puncture Abrasion (corneal)	Acute Acute
Other organs (heart, kidney, and so forth)	Puncture Contusion	Acute Acute

Injuries and Their Mechanisms—Activity 3.2 Outcome

Acute injuries	Compression	Tension	Shearing
Contusions	X		
Abrasions			X
Lacerations	X		X
Incisions	X		
Sprains		X	X
Acute strains		X	
Cartilage tears	X		X
Dislocations and subluxations	X	X	
Bone fractures	X		
Epiphyseal fractures	X	X	
Chronic injuries			
Bursitis	X	X	X
Tendinosis, tenosynovitis, and paratendinitis		X	
Stress fractures	X		

Emergency Action Steps

(50 minutes)

PURPOSE: To help you learn how to perform the emergency action steps and the Heimlich maneuver.

LEARNING OBJECTIVES

In this unit, you will learn

- what to do first when an athlete goes down due to injury or illness,
- how to perform the emergency action steps,
- how to recognize and respond to an airway blockage,
- what to do if an athlete stops breathing, and
- why learning CPR and AED is critical for a coach.

Unit Overview

Topic	Activities	Time (minutes)
A. Unit Introduction	Hear about the unit's purpose, objectives, and agenda.	1
B. Emergency Action Steps for a Responsive Athlete	Watch a DVD segment, "Performing the Emergency Action Steps." In groups of three, practice the emergency action steps for a responsive athlete.	18
C. Emergency Action Steps for an Unresponsive Athlete	In pairs, practice the emergency action steps for an unresponsive athlete.	15
D. Airway Blockage	Watch a DVD segment, "Airway Blockage." In teams, practice first aid for airway obstructions in responsive athletes, including the Heimlich maneuver.	14
E. Unit Summary	Review key unit points.	2

UNIT CONTENT

A Unit Introduction (1 minute)

- How to perform the emergency action steps for a responsive athlete
- How to perform the emergency action steps for an unresponsive athlete
- How to recognize and respond to an airway obstruction

B Emergency Action Steps for a Responsive Athlete (18 minutes)

On the DVD Segment, "Performing the Emergency Action Steps"

- Assessing the scene and the athlete
- Alerting EMS (or emergency action plan)
- Attending to the athlete's breathing

Activity 4.1 Emergency Action Steps for a Responsive Athlete

Introduction

You heard on the DVD segment what the emergency action steps are. In this activity you'll practice following those steps for a responsive athlete. To complete the activity, you'll need to know a little about first aid for a lower leg fracture. This and other illnesses and injuries are covered in the *Sport First Aid* book.

The *Sport First Aid* book includes a reference guide for over 110 sport injuries and illnesses. The description of most of these injuries and illnesses begins with four sections that will help you identify the injury or illness. These sections are as follows:

- Definition
- Causes
- Ask if Experiencing Symptoms
- Check for Signs

You'll also use the Sport First Aid Emergency Action Steps on page 28.

The emergency action steps are a one-stop guide to performing the steps, whether the athlete is responsive or unresponsive. It includes steps you should follow to

- determine if the athlete is responsive,
- check breathing, and
- follow up with appropriate first aid care.

Resources

- The Athlete, Coach, and Observer Scenarios. (These are provided after the following instructions and activity outcome.)
- Chapter 13 in *Sport First Aid*
- The Sport First Aid Emergency Action Steps located on page 28

Instructions

1. Work in groups of three. One person will be the athlete, one person will be the coach, and one person will be an observer.
2. When the activity starts, do the following:
    a. Select which role each of you will play.
    b. Spend a minute preparing for your roles.
        - If you're the athlete, read through the Athlete Scenario (see page 24) and be prepared to respond appropriately.
        - If you're the coach, read through the Coach Scenario (see page 24). You should also have chapter 13 of *Sport First Aid* open to refer to, as well as the Emergency Action Steps.
        - If you're the observer, read through the Observer Scenario (see pages 24 and 25), which you will use to evaluate the role play.
3. Start the role play.
4. After completing the role play, discuss with your group the emergency action steps that you would take.
5. You'll have 8 minutes to complete this activity.

Activity Outcome

When you're done, your group should have completed one role play. You will have practiced performing the emergency action steps for a responsive athlete.

▶ *Athlete Scenario* -

You're a gymnast who's fallen off a balance beam and broken your leg. Your leg hurts, and you heard a "pop" when you landed. There is swelling in the leg, and the leg's skin color is somewhat bluish. You try to move a bit when the coach arrives.

▶ *Coach Scenario* -

You're supervising a gymnastics workout when you see one of your athletes fall off the balance beam with a "thud." She is lying on the floor and grimacing in pain, and you see her teammates gathering around her.

To take the emergency action steps, do the following:

1. Assess the scene.
2. Assess the athlete.
3. Alert EMS or your emergency action plan.
4. Attend to the athlete.

Say out loud what you're doing as you do it.

▶ *Observer Scenario* -

Your role is to evaluate if the coach took the correct actions for each step. Use the following checklist to check off items the coach completes.

ASSESS THE SCENE

☐ Move all other players and bystanders away.

☐ Consider if the environment is safe. Do you need to move the ill or injured athlete because conditions are dangerous?

☐ Calm the athlete and keep him or her from moving.

☐ Consider if you need to roll the athlete over or remove equipment in order to evaluate his or her condition or provide first aid.

ASSESS THE ATHLETE

☐ Review in your mind how the injury or illness occurred.

☐ Review in your mind the athlete's medical history, if you know it.

☐ Check the responsiveness of the athlete by gently tapping or squeezing his or her shoulder and by asking "Are you all right, (athlete's name)?"

ALERT EMS

☐ If your assessment indicates a condition that requires medical attention, have someone call 9-1-1 or activate your emergency action plan.

ATTEND TO THE ATHLETE

☐ Identify yourself (if the athlete doesn't know you) and ask the athlete's permission to help.

☐ Make sure the athlete is fully responsive and is breathing normally (if not, begin CPR).

☐ Look for and control any severe bleeding with direct pressure.

☐ Look for normal tissue color and body temperature.

☐ While waiting for medical assistance, continue to attend to breathing, control bleeding, and monitor tissue color and body temperature.

☐ Continue to control bleeding, monitor tissue color and temperature, and help maintain the athlete's normal body temperature.

ᴄ Emergency Action Steps for an Unresponsive Athlete (15 minutes)

Activity 4.2 Emergency Action Steps for an Unresponsive Athlete

Introduction

As you just practiced, once you've established it is safe to treat the athlete, you should check the athlete's breathing. In this activity, you'll practice checking an *unresponsive* athlete's breathing and practice CPR/AED procedures.

To complete the activity, you'll use the Sport First Aid Emergency Action Steps located on page 28 in your workbook.

One of the actions you'll need to take with an unresponsive athlete is to check breathing. When checking for breathing, do so for no more than 10 seconds.

Resources

• The Emergency Action Steps for an Unresponsive Athlete Scenario (provided after the following instructions and activity outcome)

• The Sport First Aid Emergency Action Steps located on page 28

Instructions

1. Work in pairs.
2. First review the Emergency Action Steps for an Unresponsive Athlete Scenario, and then follow the steps in the scenario, using the Sport First Aid Emergency Action Steps to guide what you do.

    a. One partner plays the role of a softball player who has collapsed on the field. The athlete is unresponsive. This person should lie on his or her back and breathe normally.

    b. The other partner plays the role of the coach and performs the emergency action steps.

3. When the coach has completed the emergency action steps, reverse roles and repeat the entire scenario so that both partners have a chance to practice all skills.
4. You'll have 10 minutes to complete this activity, with each person in the coach's role for 5 minutes.

Activity Outcome

When you're done, you should have practiced performing the emergency action steps for an unresponsive athlete.

▶ *Emergency Action Steps for an Unresponsive Athlete Scenario* - - - - - -

In the second inning, your softball team has just made a play, but you now notice that several players are standing around one of your team members, who's lying face up on the ground. You run out to check if she's responsive, but she is not. None of the players knows exactly what happened.

1. Take initial first aid steps.

   a. Check for response.

      • Coach: Tap the athlete on the shoulder and ask "Are you all right, (athlete's name)?"

      Athlete: Do not respond.

   b. Send helper to call 911 and get the AED.

      • Since no helper is present in this role play, pretend to send someone.

      • Tell the helper to provide information regarding the location and address, type of injury, and the first aid being administered.

2. Check the athlete's breathing for no more than 10 seconds.

3. Assume you are unable to detect the athlete breathing. Pretend to practice CPR/AED procedures.

4. Reverse roles and repeat the entire activity so that both partners have a chance to practice all skills.

Emergency Action Steps

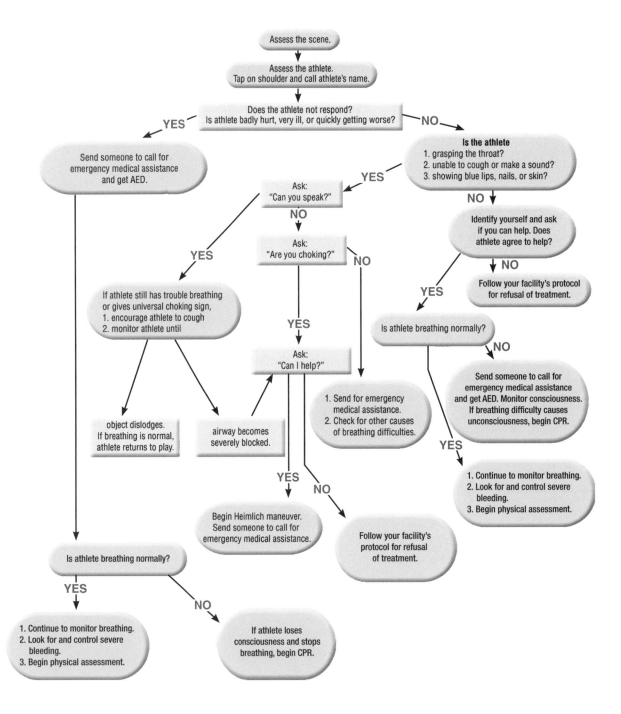

Assess the scene.

Assess the athlete.
Tap on shoulder and call athlete's name.

Does the athlete not respond?
Is athlete badly hurt, very ill, or quickly getting worse?

YES — Send someone to call for emergency medical assistance and get AED.

NO — **Is the athlete**
1. grasping the throat?
2. unable to cough or make a sound?
3. showing blue lips, nails, or skin?

YES — Ask: "Can you speak?"

NO — Identify yourself and ask if you can help. Does athlete agree to help?

NO — Ask: "Can you speak?"

YES — If athlete still has trouble breathing or gives universal choking sign,
1. encourage athlete to cough
2. monitor athlete until

NO — Ask: "Are you choking?"

NO (Identify yourself...) — Follow your facility's protocol for refusal of treatment.

YES (Identify yourself...) — Is athlete breathing normally?

NO (Are you choking?) — 1. Send for emergency medical assistance. 2. Check for other causes of breathing difficulties.

YES (Are you choking?) — Ask: "Can I help?"

object dislodges. If breathing is normal, athlete returns to play.

airway becomes severely blocked.

YES (Can I help?) — Begin Heimlich maneuver. Send someone to call for emergency medical assistance.

NO (Can I help?) — Follow your facility's protocol for refusal of treatment.

Is athlete breathing normally?

NO (Is athlete breathing normally? right) — Send someone to call for emergency medical assistance and get AED. Monitor consciousness. If breathing difficulty causes unconsciousness, begin CPR.

YES (Is athlete breathing normally? right) — 1. Continue to monitor breathing. 2. Look for and control severe bleeding. 3. Begin physical assessment.

YES (Is athlete breathing normally? left) — 1. Continue to monitor breathing. 2. Look for and control severe bleeding. 3. Begin physical assessment.

NO (Is athlete breathing normally? left) — If athlete loses consciousness and stops breathing, begin CPR.

D Airway Blockage (14 minutes)

On the DVD Segment, "Airway Blockage"

- How to recognize and respond to an airway blockage
  - Mild and severe airway blockage in a responsive athlete (includes performing the Heimlich maneuver)
  - Severe airway blockage in an unresponsive athlete

Activity 4.3 Airway Blockage in a Responsive Athlete

Introduction

During this activity, you'll practice providing first aid care for severe airway blockage in a responsive athlete.

Resources

- The Airway Blockage Scenario (provided after the following instructions and activity outcome)

Instructions

1. Work in pairs.
2. Read the introduction to the Airway Blockage Scenario, and then follow the numbered instructions.
3. One person will play the role of the athlete; the other person will play the role of the coach who is responding to the situation.
4. When the coach has responded to the severe airway blockage, reverse roles and repeat the entire scenario so that both partners have a chance to practice all skills.
5. You'll have 8 minutes to complete this activity, with each person in the coach's role for 4 minutes.

Activity Outcome

When you're done, you should have practiced providing first aid care (including the Heimlich maneuver) for severe airway blockage in a responsive athlete.

▶ *Airway Obstruction Scenario* -

A basketball player (your partner) is grasping his or her throat, giving the universal choking sign. The athlete is coughing and gasping. The athlete had been chewing gum. You provide first aid care for this athlete, who has a *mild airway blockage*, and this is what happens:

- You ask, "Are you okay?" The athlete says "yes" but has trouble breathing and gives the universal choking sign.
- You encourage the athlete to cough.
- You monitor the athlete, hoping the object will be dislodged and the athlete will begin to breathe normally.

Unfortunately, the basketball player's situation gets worse. The athlete still exhibits the universal choking sign, but the airway becomes severely blocked, and the athlete is unable to cough or speak. Provide first aid care for this athlete, who now has a *total airway blockage.*

1. Coach: Ask, "Are you choking?"

   Athlete: Shake your head "yes," or give the universal choking signal.

2. Coach: Ask, "Can I help?"

   Athlete: Shake your head "yes."

3. Coach: Begin the Heimlich maneuver. Practice the correct hand position and placement, *but only simulate the thrusts rather than actually performing them fully.*

   a. Stand behind the athlete, if an adult, and kneel if a child.

   b. Make a fist. Place the thumb side against the athlete's abdomen, just above the navel (see figure 4.4, page 56 in *Sport First Aid*

   c. Give quick inward and upward thrusts.

   d. Continue the compressions until

      1. the object is expelled; or

      2. the athlete loses responsiveness from lack of air, then do CPR.

   Athlete: Pretend your gum is dislodged and you're able to start breathing again.

4. Reverse roles and repeat the entire activity so that both partners have a chance to practice all skills.

The Heimlich Maneuver

- As discussed in the *Sport First Aid* book, it's very important to use the correct hand position and placement for the Heimlich maneuver.
- The Heimlich maneuver should not be performed on infants under 1.
- Only health care providers should perform the Heimlich maneuver on unresponsive victims.
- If the athlete is choking but shakes his or her head "no" when you ask if you can help, send for emergency medical assistance and assess for other causes of the breathing difficulties. These are discussed in chapter 7 of *Sport First Aid.*

E Unit Summary (2 minutes)

- When an athlete goes down due to an injury or illness, the first thing you should do is quickly assess the scene and the athlete.
- After quickly assessing the scene and the athlete, and alerting EMS if necessary, attend to the athlete's breathing. Attending to breathing is done differently depending on whether the athlete is responsive or unresponsive.
- Maintaining breathing and circulation is the top priority.
- The first aid care that you provide will differ if the airway is mildly blocked versus severely blocked and if the athlete is responsive or unresponsive.
- If an athlete is not breathing, begin CPR.
- All coaches should become CPR and AED certified. Become certified by or attending certification classes offered by the following agencies: American Red Cross, American Heart Association, or National Safety Council.

(Notes)

Unit 4 Activity Outcome

ASSESS THE SCENE

1. The coach moves all the teammates away.
2. The coach considers if the environment is safe and whether to move the athlete.
3. The coach calms the athlete and keeps her from moving.
4. The coach considers whether there's a need to move or roll the athlete over.

ASSESS THE ATHLETE

1. The coach reviews in his or her mind how the injury occurred.
2. The coach reviews in his or her mind the athlete's medical history.
3. The coach checks the athlete's responsiveness by asking "Are you all right, (athlete's name)?"

   (Tapping the shoulder isn't necessary, since the athlete is obviously moving.)

ALERT EMS

It appears that the athlete's leg is badly hurt, so the coach either calls EMS (9-1-1) or sends an assistant to do so.

ATTEND TO THE ATHLETE

1. The coach asks the athlete's permission to help.
2. The coach checks to make sure the athlete is fully responsive and is breathing normally.
3. The coach looks for any severe bleeding.
4. The coach looks at the athlete's tissue color and body temperature.
5. While waiting for medical assistance, the coach continues to attend to the athlete's breathing and monitors her tissue color and body temperature (in case of shock).
6. The coach helps the athlete maintain normal body temperature by covering her with a blanket.

Physical Assessment and Providing Immediate First Aid

(60 minutes)

PURPOSE: To help you learn how to conduct a physical assessment, control bleeding, minimize shock, splint unstable injuries, and respond to heat-related illnesses.

LEARNING OBJECTIVES

In this unit, you will learn

- how to perform a physical assessment of an injured or ill athlete,
- how to control arterial and venous (profuse) bleeding and capillary (slow, steady) bleeding,
- what methods to use in minimizing shock,
- how to splint unstable injuries,
- how to use the PRICE method to minimize local tissue damage, and
- how to respond to heat-related illnesses.

Unit Overview

Topic	Activities	Time (minutes)
A. Unit Introduction	Hear about the unit's purpose, objectives, and agenda.	1
B. Physical Assessment	Watch a DVD segment, "Physical Assessment: History, Inspection, and Touch."	7
C. Controlling Bleeding and Protecting Against Blood-Borne Pathogens	Watch a DVD segment, "Controlling Bleeding." Practice three methods of controlling bleeding.	17
D. Controlling Tissue Damage (Shock), Applying Splints, and Applying Compression Wraps	Watch a DVD segment, "Shock, Splints, and Compression Wraps." As a class, practice positioning an ill or injured athlete. In pairs, practice splinting and applying compression wraps.	28
E. Exertional Heat-Related Illnesses	Watch a DVD segment "Responding to Heat-Related Illnesses."	5
F. Unit Summary	Review key unit points.	2

UNIT CONTENT

A Unit Introduction (1 minute)

- Conducting the physical assessment
- Types of bleeding and how to control bleeding
- Treating shock
- Splinting
- Applying compression wraps
- Using PRICE—protection, rest, ice, compression, and elevation—to minimize local tissue damage
- Responding to heat-related illnesses

B Physical Assessment (7 minutes)

Sport First Aid Physical Assessment Steps

The Sport First Aid Physical Assessment Steps are located on page 38 in the workbook. This figure provides a quick reminder of how to conduct a physical assessment. It includes steps you should follow to

- determine the history of the injury or illness,
- inspect the athlete for symptoms and signs of injury or illness, and
- use the sense of touch to feel for additional symptoms and signs of injury or illness.

As you watch the DVD segment, refer to the Sport First Aid Physical Assessment Steps.

On the DVD Segment, "Physical Assessment: History, Inspection, and Touch"

- The physical assessment: HIT
  - History
  - Inspection
  - Touch
- Overview of basic sport first aid techniques

C Controlling Bleeding and Protecting Against Blood-Borne Pathogens (17 minutes)

On the DVD Segment, "Controlling Bleeding"

- Preventing blood-borne pathogen transmission
- Causes, signs, and symptoms of profuse (arterial and venous) and slow, steady (capillary) bleeding
- Controlling arterial and venous bleeding
- Controlling slow, steady bleeding
- Playing it safe with bleeding injuries

Emergency Action Steps

History

Determine:

   injury location,
   whether a reinjury,
   injury mechanism, or
   symptoms (e.g., headache,
   pain, or numbness).

↓

Inspection

Look for:

   bleeding,
   skin appearance,
   pupil size and reaction,
   deformities,
   vomiting or coughing,
   swelling,
   discoloration,
   ability to walk,
   position of an upper
   extremity, or
   pulse rate.

↓

Touch

Feel for:
   point tenderness,
   skin temperature,
   sensation or numbness, or
   deformity.

Activity 5.1 Controlling Bleeding

Introduction

As you heard on the DVD segment, there are three main ways to control bleeding:

- Cover the wound with sterile gauze pads.
- Apply direct pressure.
- Apply elastic roller gauze or elastic bandage over the gauze pads.

In this activity, you'll practice these methods of controlling bleeding.

Resources

- The Controlling Bleeding Scenario (provided after the following instructions and activity outcome)
- Disposable gloves (one pair for each coach)
- Gauze pads (three for each coach)
- Elastic wrap or roller gauze (one for each coach)

Instructions

1. Work in pairs. One person will be the athlete, and one person will be the coach.
2. First review the Controlling Bleeding Scenario, and then follow the steps in the scenario.
3. When the coach has completed the scenario, reverse roles and repeat the entire scenario so that both partners have a chance to practice all skills.
4. You'll have 7 minutes to complete this activity, with each person in the coach's role for a little under 4 minutes.

Activity Outcome

When you're done, you should have completed the Controlling Bleeding Scenario two times—with each person having played the role of the coach.

▶ *Controlling Bleeding Scenario* -

The athlete (your partner) has a bleeding injury suffered while diving to save a volleyball. The athlete's wrist hit the volleyball standard, leaving a deep gash below the palm. You've completed the physical assessment and identified one injury requiring immediate attention: the bleeding wrist. After sending for medical assistance and putting a pair of disposable gloves on your hands, administer first aid for profuse bleeding.

1. Cover the wound with sterile gauze pads.
2. Apply firm, direct pressure over the wound with your hand. (The bleeding does not stop.)
3. Apply elastic roller gauze or elastic bandage over the gauze pads. Make sure it's not so tight that a finger can't be slipped under the bandage. (The bleeding stops.)
4. Leave the gauze in place, add more gauze if necessary, and cover with roller gauze or elastic wrap.
5. Monitor breathing until medical assistance arrives.

D Controlling Tissue Damage (Shock), Applying Splints, and Applying Compression Wraps (28 minutes)

On the DVD Segment, "Shock, Splints, and Compression Wraps"

- Shock: definition, its effects, causes, symptoms, signs, first aid steps
- Playing it safe when treating for shock
- Splinting: when, what, and how to splint (with demonstration)
- Playing it safe with splinting
- Local tissue damage: causes, symptoms, signs
- PRICE: definition and demonstration, including demonstration of compression wraps
- Types of ice applications (demonstration) and guidelines for applying each
- Contraindications to applying ice
- Playing it safe with applying heat

Activity 5.2 Positioning an Ill or Injured Athlete

Introduction

As you heard on the DVD segment, if the athlete is in shock, you may need to position the athlete properly. This also holds for other types of injuries and medical conditions.

- Proper positioning of an injured athlete depends on whether the athlete is injured or not, has a head or spine injury, is responsive or unresponsive, is breathing, or is in shock.
- In this activity, we'll decide as a class how to position an ill or injured athlete.

Resources

- The Positioning an Ill or Injured Athlete Scenarios on page 42
- The table, Positions for Ill or Injured Athletes, on page 43

Instructions

1. We'll work together as a class.
2. We'll have two volunteers who will play the role of ill or injured athletes.
3. We'll use the Positioning an Ill or Injured Athlete Scenarios and the table, Positions for Ill or Injured Athletes, on pages 42-43 in the workbook to decide how to position each of our volunteer athletes.
4. We have about 8 minutes for this activity.

Activity Outcome

When we're done, we will have positioned two ill or injured athletes in the correct position for their conditions.

▶ *Positioning an Ill or Injured Athlete Scenario 1* - - - - - - - - - - - - - -

A football player is lying on the ground. You did not see the injury occur. He is responsive. You check the athlete's breathing and find that the athlete is breathing normally.

You begin the physical assessment by asking the athlete what caused the injury. In a groggy voice, the athlete answers that he had run into a lineman head first. You ask the athlete if he heard a pop, crack, or other noise. The athlete tells you that he only heard his helmet as he hit the ground. The athlete doesn't have a clear idea of where he hurts, but he does tell you that his head snapped and his fingers are tingly. His head hurts, his ears are ringing, and he feels nauseated. He also says he's having trouble seeing, that everything's blurry.

1. In what position should you place the athlete? Why?

▶ *Positioning an Ill or Injured Athlete Scenario 2* - - - - - - - - - - - - - -

A rowing crew team member slips on the dock and falls, grazing his leg on a sharp post that deeply lacerates his leg. The cut is bleeding rapidly, and the blood looks dark red. The athlete is lying flat on his back on the dock. You have put on goggles and gloves and have covered the wound with gauze pads. While you hold the pads down with firm, direct pressure, you examine the athlete and notice that he's breathing more slowly than usual, his pupils are dilated, and he's sweating. You ask him how he's feeling, and he says he feels weak and thirsty and would like a drink.

1. Is it necessary to reposition the athlete? Why?
2. Should you give the athlete something to drink? Why or why not?

Positions for Ill or Injured Athletes

CONDITION	POSITION	RATIONALE
Responsive athlete with suspected spinal injury	Manually stabilize the head so that the head, neck, and spine do not move and are kept in line (see figure 5.5).	Pain and loss of function usually accompany a spinal injury, but the absence of pain does not mean that the athlete has not been significantly injured. If you suspect an athlete could possibly have a spinal injury, assume he or she does.
Unresponsive, uninjured athlete who is breathing, but having difficulty with secretions or vomiting	Recovery position	Protects airway by allowing fluid to drain easily from the mouth.
Unresponsive, injured athlete who is breathing, but having difficulty with secretions or vomiting OR who you must leave unattended to get help	Modified recovery position (HAINES)	Protects airway by allowing fluid to drain easily from the mouth. Using the HAINES position, there is less neck movement and less risk of spinal-cord damage.
Unresponsive athlete who is not breathing (or you are unsure)	Flat on the back for CPR	Occasional gasps are not normal and are not capable of supplying the athlete with enough oxygen to sustain life.
Responsive or unresponsive athlete with signs and symptoms of shock from severe bleeding	Flat on the back	It is best to leave the athlete lying flat. If athlete is having difficulty with secretions or vomiting, place in the recovery position. If spinal injury is suspected, use the HAINES position.

Activity 5.3 Splinting and Compression Wraps

Introduction

Now let's practice applying splints and compression wraps.

Resources

- The Splinting Scenario and Compression Wrap Scenario (see pages 44 to 45)
- Chapter 5 of *Sport First Aid*
- Rigid, padded splints for a broken arm (enough for half the class)
- Pillows, sweatshirts, or towels for the splinting activity (enough for half the class)
- Ties or elastic wrap to secure a splint (enough for half the class)
- Elastic wrap to secure a splint to the body and to use for a compression wrap (enough for half the class)

Instructions

1. Work in pairs. One person will be the athlete, and one person will be the coach. You'll complete two scenarios.

2. First review the Splinting Scenario, and then follow the steps in the scenario.

3. When the coach has completed the Splinting Scenario, reverse roles and repeat the scenario so that both partners have a chance to practice all skills.

4. Then review the Compression Wrap Scenario, and follow the steps in the scenario.

5. When the coach has completed the Compression Wrap Scenario, reverse roles and repeat the scenario so that both partners have a chance to practice all skills.

6. You'll have 15 minutes to do this activity. You should spend about 10 minutes splinting (5 minutes for each person) and 5 minutes applying the compression wrap (2 and a half minutes for each person).

Activity Outcome

When you're done, both of you should have practiced splinting a broken arm and applying a compression wrap to a sprained ankle.

▶ Splinting Scenario -

Your partner is a gymnast who has suffered a possible fractured forearm, just below the elbow. The injured arm is straight and held near the athlete's side. You have already completed a physical assessment. You find out that the arrival of EMS will be delayed for more than 20 minutes, so you apply a splint to the area.

1. Leave the arm in the position that you found it.

2. Place a pillow, sweatshirt, or towel between the arm and the body to help support the arm.

3. Immobilize the arm from the hand to above the elbow joint using a rigid, padded splint.

4. Secure the splint with ties or an elastic wrap. Place ties above and below the injury, but not directly over it. Apply light, even pressure with the wrap, so as not to press directly upon the injury.

5. Immobilize the entire arm, securing it to the body with an elastic wrap.

6. Check the radial pulse.

7. Compare your splint with the one shown in figure 5.8, page 72, of *Sport First Aid.*

8. Reverse roles and repeat the entire scenario so that both partners have a chance to practice all skills.

▶ Compression Wrap Scenario- -

Your partner is a softball player who twisted her ankle running to first base. You have already completed a physical assessment and have begun the PRICE sequence. You have protected the athlete from further movement, helped her to the bench where she can rest, removed her shoe, and applied an ice bag for 15 minutes. Now apply a compression wrap.

1. Start the wrap just above the toes.

2. Wrap upward (toward the heart), in an overlapping spiral, starting with even and somewhat snug pressure, then gradually wrapping looser once above the injury.

3. Periodically check the skin color, temperature, and sensation of the injured area to make sure that the wrap isn't compressing any nerves or arteries. Wraps that are too tight can reduce blood flow to the area and cause tissue damage.

4. Compare your compression wrap with the one shown in figure 5.17, page 78, of *Sport First Aid.*

5. Reverse roles and repeat the entire scenario so that both partners have a chance to practice all skills.

E Exertional Heat-Related Illnesses (5 minutes)

On the DVD Segment, "Responding to Heat-Related Illnesses"

- Heat cramps
- Heat exhaustion
- Heatstroke

F Unit Summary (2 minutes)

- After you've established that the athlete is breathing, you should conduct the physical assessment to determine the nature, site, and severity of an injury or illness.
- Remember the acronym HIT—which stands for history, inspection, and touch. This will help you complete a thorough physical assessment.
- After completing the physical assessment, you should attend to these issues, in this order of priority:

  1. Control profuse external bleeding.
  2. Minimize shock.
  3. Splint unstable injuries.
  4. Use the PRICE method to minimize local tissue damage.

- PRICE stands for protection, rest, ice, compression, and elevation.
- When an athlete suffers a heat-related illness, prompt action is key. If the athlete shows signs of possible heatstroke, send for emergency medical assistance and immediately cool the athlete in a wading pool or tub filled with ice water.

(Notes)

Unit 5 Activity Outcomes

▶ *Emergency Action Steps—Activity 5.2 Outcome* - - - - - - - - - - - - - -

POSITIONING AN ILL OR INJURED ATHLETE SCENARIO 1

1. In what position should you place the athlete? Why?

Because he has a potential head or spine injury, this athlete's head and neck should be immobilized with the athlete lying face up and flat on the ground.

POSITIONING AN ILL OR INJURED ATHLETE SCENARIO 2

1. Is it necessary to reposition the athlete? Why?

This athlete should remain flat on his back, as he seems to be going into shock from severe bleeding. (Do not raise his legs; this was once advocated, but current evidence does not support this practice.) However, if you think he may be about to vomit, you may want to move him into the recovery position. If you reposition the athlete, you'll need to maintain direct pressure on the wound to continue controlling the bleeding.

2. Should you give the athlete something to drink? Why or why not?

This athlete should not be given anything to drink. You should not give fluids to an athlete who is suffering from shock. Doing so can cause vomiting or choking.

Moving Injured or Sick Athletes

(10 minutes)

PURPOSE: To help you learn how to determine whether and how an injured or sick athlete should be moved.

LEARNING OBJECTIVES

In this unit, you will learn

- how to determine whether an athlete should be moved;
- how to decide who should move an athlete and how the athlete should be moved; and
- how to do the four- or five-person rescue, the one-person drag, the one-person walking assist, the two-person walking assist, the four-handed carrying assist, and the two-handed carrying assist.

Unit Overview

Topic	Activities	Time (minutes)
A. Unit Introduction	Hear about the unit's purpose, objectives, and agenda.	1
B. Moving an Athlete	Watch a DVD segment, "Moving Injured or Sick Athletes." Practice techniques for moving athletes.	8
C. Unit Summary	Review key unit points.	1

UNIT CONTENT

A Unit Introduction (1 minute)

- Whether to move an athlete
- Playing it safe when moving athletes
- Techniques for moving critically injured and noncritically injured athletes

B Moving an Athlete (8 minutes)

On the DVD Segment, "Moving Injured or Sick Athletes"

- To move or not to move an athlete
- Playing it safe when moving critically injured, unresponsive athletes
- Techniques for moving critically injured athletes: four- or five-person rescue and one-person drag
- Playing it safe when moving noncritically injured athletes
- Techniques for moving noncritically injured athletes: one-person walking assist, two-person walking assist, four-handed carrying assist, and two-handed carrying assist
- Playing it safe to protect yourself

Activity 6.1 Moving an Athlete

Introduction

To move an athlete safely, you need to know how to correctly perform each technique. In this activity, you'll get to practice three techniques for moving athletes.

Resources

- The Two-Person Walking Assist Scenario, and Two-Handed Carrying Assist Scenario (provided after the following instructions and activity outcome)
- Pages 85 and 86 in the *Sport First Aid* book, which show photos of each technique

Instructions

1. Work in groups of three to four.
2. First review the Two-Person Walking Assist Scenario and Two-Handed Carrying Assist Scenario, and then follow the steps in each scenario.
3. All members of your group should practice the techniques.
4. Take 4 to 5 minutes to complete this activity.

Activity Outcome

When you're done, you should have practiced as many of the techniques as possible: the two-person walking assist and the two-handed carrying assist.

▶ Two-Person Walking Assist Scenario -

An athlete is sitting down on the field, but otherwise shows no sign of injury. He complains of being slightly dazed from contact with an opposing player. The technique you should use to move the athlete to the sideline is the **TWO-PERSON WALKING ASSIST.**

1. Kneel on one knee on opposite sides of the athlete.
2. Place the athlete's arms around you (and your partner) and instruct the athlete to hold onto your shoulders.
3. Hold the athlete around the waist.
4. On the count of three, bring the athlete to a standing position.
5. Slowly walk to the sidelines, supporting the athlete with your arms and shoulders.

▶ Two-Handed Carrying Assist Scenario - - - - - - - - - - - - - - - - - - -

An athlete has a badly strained calf muscle and is unable to walk or help support her weight. The technique you should use to move the athlete is the **TWO-HANDED CARRYING ASSIST,** which requires two people.

1. Stand behind the injured athlete, facing your partner.
2. Grasp each other's forearms nearest the athlete.
3. Instruct the athlete to sit on your and your partner's arms and to put his or her arms around your shoulders.
4. Support the athlete's back with your free arms.
5. Slowly lift the athlete by straightening your legs.

c Unit Summary (1 minute)

- Before moving an athlete, determine if it is necessary and safe to do so.
- If an athlete must be moved, carefully decide which method should be used to move the athlete.
- For critically injured athletes, consider the four- or five-person rescue, or the one-person drag.
- For noncritically injured athletes, consider the one-person walking assist, two-person walking assist, four-handed carrying assist, and two-handed carrying assist.

(Notes)

Head, Spine, and Nerve Injuries

(20 minutes)

PURPOSE: To help you learn how to identify and provide first aid care for head, spine, and nerve injuries.

LEARNING OBJECTIVES

In this unit, you will learn

- how to recognize the signs and symptoms of head, spine, and nerve injuries,
- what type of first aid to provide for head, spine, or nerve injuries, and
- strategies to use in your sport first aid game plan to prevent head, spine, and nerve injuries.

Unit Overview

Topic	Activities	Time (minutes)
A. Unit Introduction	Hear about the unit's purpose, objectives, and agenda.	1
B. First Aid for Head and Spine Injuries	Watch a DVD segment, "Responding to Head and Spine Injuries." Practice identifying head and spine injuries and determining the first aid steps needed.	18
C. Unit Summary	Review key unit points.	1

UNIT CONTENT

A Unit Introduction (I minute)

- Identifying head and spine injuries
- Determining what first aid steps to take
- Steps you can take to help prevent head and spine injuries

B First Aid for Head and Spine Injuries (18 minutes)

On the DVD Segment, "Responding to Head and Spine Injuries"

- Head injuries
- Spine injuries
- Evaluation and care of head and spine injuries

Part III of Sport First Aid

- Read the introduction to part III, page 89, in *Sport First Aid*.
- Over 110 different conditions are covered.
- The chapters are ordered from life-threatening conditions to serious then minor problems.
- For each condition, detailed information is given, including symptoms, signs, and first aid steps.

Activity 7.1 Head and Spine Injuries

Introduction

The key with head and spine injuries is to recognize that an athlete may have such an injury. Once you have determined that an athlete may have a head or spine injury, the first aid care you provide will be quite similar for either type.

Resources

- The Head and Spine Injury Scenarios (provided after the following instructions and activity outcome)
- Chapter 8 of *Sport First Aid,* which begins on page 101

Instructions

1. Work in teams of two to four.
2. Read the Head and Spine Injury Scenarios, and answer the questions posed.
3. This is a team competition; teams will be awarded points for correct answers.
4. Take 8 minutes to complete your work.

Activity Outcome

When you're done, you should have identified the possible injury in each scenario and the first aid steps you would take to care for the injury.

► *Head and Spine Injury Scenario 1* -

Two soccer players collide with their heads while going for a ball. One athlete falls to the ground and is not moving. When you reach the athlete, you find she is breathing, but she is unresponsive.

1. What injury do you believe this athlete has? Use chapter 8 of *Sport First Aid,* pages 101 to 110, to help make your decision.

2. What first aid steps would you take to care for this injury? Record the steps in the space below.

▶ *Head and Spine Injury Scenario 2* -

You observe one of your football players getting his neck twisted after an opposing player grabs his face mask. He falls to the ground and is not moving. When you reach the athlete, he is breathing and responsive, but he is unable to move his extremities.

1. What injury do you believe this athlete has? Use chapter 8 of *Sport First Aid,* pages 101 to 110, to help make your decision.

2. What first aid steps would you take to care for this injury? Record the steps in the space below.

C Unit Summary (1 minute)

- There is no such thing as a minor brain or spine injury. Even minor blows can injure the brain and should not be taken lightly.
- Regardless of the head or spine injury, the first aid response is very similar.
- If an athlete is responsive but exhibits any signs or symptoms of a head injury, remove the athlete from play. Assign someone to monitor the athlete and send for emergency medical assistance if signs or symptoms worsen. For a suspected mild concussion, notify the parents. Ask them to monitor the athlete, and give them a checklist of head injury signs and symptoms. Instruct them to take the athlete to a physician.
- If you suspect a head or spine injury in a football player, do not attempt to remove the athlete's helmet.

(Notes)

Unit 7 Activity Outcome

HEAD AND SPINE INJURY SCENARIO 1

- *Injury:* The athlete most likely has a head injury.
- *First aid steps:*
    1. Send for emergency medical assistance. **2 PT**
    2. Immobilize the athlete's head and spine. **2 PTS**
    3. Monitor breathing and provide CPR if needed. **2 PTS**
    4. Control profuse bleeding. **2 PTS**
    5. Treat for shock as needed. **2 PTS**
    6. Stabilize any fractures or unstable injuries. **2 PTS**

TOTAL POINTS POSSIBLE: 12

HEAD AND SPINE INJURY SCENARIO 2

- *Injury:* The athlete most likely has a spine injury.
- *First aid steps:*
    1. Send for emergency medical assistance. **2 PTS**
    2. Immobilize the athlete's head and spine. **2 PTS**
    3. Monitor breathing and provide CPR if needed. **2 PTS**
    4. Control profuse bleeding. **2 PTS**
    5. Treat for shock as needed. **2 PTS**
    6. Stabilize or let EMS stabilize any fractures or unstable injuries. **2 PTS**

TOTAL POINTS POSSIBLE: 24

Each first aid step is worth 2 points, for a total of 24 points for both injuries.

Musculoskeletal Injuries

(35 minutes)

PURPOSE: To help you learn how to identify and provide first aid care for the most common sprains, strains, fractures, and dislocations.

LEARNING OBJECTIVES

In this unit, you will learn

- how to recognize common musculoskeletal injuries and
- how to provide first aid care for sprains, strains, fractures, and dislocations.

Unit Overview

Topic	Activities	Time (minutes)
A. Unit Introduction	Hear about the unit's purpose, objectives, and agenda.	1
B. Recognizing and Caring for Common Musculoskeletal Injuries	Watch a DVD segment, "Musculoskeletal Injuries." Practice identifying common musculoskeletal injuries and taking the first aid steps needed.	32
C. Unit Summary	Review key unit points.	2

UNIT CONTENT

A Unit Introduction (1 minute)

- The main types of musculoskeletal injuries
- Identifying musculoskeletal injuries to various body parts
- Determining what first aid steps to take

B Recognizing and Caring for Common Musculoskeletal Injuries (32 minutes)

On the DVD Segment, "Musculoskeletal Injuries"

- Commonly occurring musculoskeletal injuries
- The main types of musculoskeletal injuries
- General first aid steps to take with these injuries

Activity 8.1 Musculoskeletal Injuries

Introduction

Musculoskeletal injuries are the most frequent first aid problem you will face. In this activity, you'll practice identifying injuries, and you'll write a list of first aid steps you would take for each injury.

Resources

- The Musculoskeletal Injury Scenarios (provided after the following instructions and activity outcome)
- Chapters 12 and 13 of *Sport First Aid*. Chapter 12 begins on page 147.

Instructions

1. Work in teams of two to four.

2. Read the Musculoskeletal Injury Scenarios, and answer the questions posed.

3. This is another team competition. Points will be awarded for correct answers: 2 points for correctly identifying the injury, 1 point for correctly identifying the severity or Grade (if there is one), and 3 points for including all first aid steps. Your team will receive 0 points for the first aid section unless *all* steps are included. There are 34 possible points.

4. You'll have 24 minutes to complete this activity.

Activity Outcome

When you're done, you should have identified the injury in each scenario and the first aid steps you would take to care for each injury. Points will be awarded for correct injury identification and first aid steps.

▶ *Musculoskeletal Injury Scenario 1* -

One of your swimmers comes to you after practice complaining of a sore shoulder. You ask a few questions and find that the swimmer's shoulder hurts when he lifts his arm overhead. In your physical assessment, you examine his shoulder with your fingers and find that he has mild tenderness over the front of his shoulder. He has been swimming with the sore shoulder for a week and has just now mentioned the problem. You had not noticed any change in his swimming performance.

1. What injury do you believe this athlete has? Use chapter 12 of *Sport First Aid,* pages 147 to 160, to help make your decision.

2. Is this injury a Grade I, II, or III injury?

3. What first aid steps would you take to care for this injury? Record the steps in the space below.

▶ Musculoskeletal Injury Scenario 2 -

Your softball pitcher is hit hard in the upper trunk by the ball. She crumples in pain. Her breathing is normal, but she has pain when she breathes deeply or laughs. The athlete experiences pain when you gently compress the rib cage.

1. What injury do you believe this athlete has? Use chapter 12 of *Sport First Aid,* pages 160 to 161, to help make your decision.

2. What first aid steps would you take to care for this injury? Record the steps in the space below.

▶ Musculoskeletal Injury Scenario 3 -

Your star wrestler seems to have hurt his middle finger while catching himself during a fall. The wrestler says he felt a pop and that his finger feels "loose." He is unable to fully bend his finger. You can see that the finger is swollen and deformed, and when you touch the joint, the wrestler grimaces in pain.

1. What injury do you believe this athlete has? Use chapter 12 of *Sport First Aid,* pages 175 to 182, to help make your decision.

2. What first aid steps would you take to care for this injury? Record the steps in the space below.

▶ *Musculoskeletal Injury Scenario 4* -

When the kicker on your football team pulls up short after a punt, you know something is wrong. You and your assistant jog out on the field and help the player walk to the sidelines. The athlete has moderate pain when trying to extend his thigh backward or bend his knee. The back of his thigh is tender, and you can feel a slight indentation there.

1. What injury do you believe this athlete has? Use chapter 13 of *Sport First Aid,* pages 190 to 201, to help make your decision.

2. Is this injury a Grade I, II, or III injury?

3. What first aid steps would you take to care for this injury? Record the steps in the space below.

▶ *Musculoskeletal Injury Scenario 5* -

The guard on your girls' basketball team lost her footing and twisted her knee as she scrambled to reposition for a play. You quickly substituted another player so that she could come off the court. The athlete says she didn't hear or feel a pop, but she has mild pain when she tries to straighten her knee. There is no swelling.

1. What injury do you believe this athlete has? Use chapter 13 of *Sport First Aid,* pages 201 to 209, to help make your decision.

2. Is this injury a Grade I, II, or III injury?

3. What first aid steps would you take to care for this injury? Record the steps in the space below.

▶ *Musculoskeletal Injury Scenario 6* -

One of your volleyball players landed wrong coming down from a spike. Her foot rolled inward, and she is writhing in pain. Her breathing and circulation are normal, but her ankle is swelling rapidly and she cannot walk on it. Her ankle has no obvious deformity, and she experiences no pain when you squeeze above or below the injury. She has no tingling or numbness, and her toes and toenails are normal in color. Her point tenderness seems isolated to just below the ankle bones, but the pain there is severe.

1. What injury do you believe this athlete has? Use chapter 13 of *Sport First Aid,* pages 209 to 223, to help make your decision.

2. Is this injury a Grade I, II, or III injury?

3. What first aid steps would you take to care for this injury? Record the steps in the space below.

C Unit Summary (2 minutes)

- You will likely deal with musculoskeletal injuries more than any other type of injury.
- Chapters 12 and 13 of *Sport First Aid* can be used for guidance in identifying and providing first aid care for musculoskeletal injuries.
- Once the injury is identified, the first aid steps are similar regardless of the type and severity of injury:
  - For Grade I sprains and strains, rest the athlete from painful activities, apply ice, and refer the athlete to a physician if symptoms and signs worsen or do not subside within a few days.

- For Grade II and III sprains and strains, rest the athlete from all activities, prevent the athlete from using the injured part (if a Grade III sprain or strain, be sure to immobilize the injured part with a splint and possibly a sling), monitor and treat for shock if needed and send for emergency medical assistance if it occurs, and apply ice and send to a physician if shock does not occur.

- For fractures, immobilize the injured part, apply ice, and send for emergency medical assistance if bones are grossly displaced or protruding.

(Notes)

Unit 8 Activity Outcome

MUSCULOSKELETAL INJURY SCENARIO 1

- *Injury:* Rotator cuff strain. **2 PTS**
- *Severity:* Grade I. **1 PT**
- *First aid steps:* 1. Rest from painful activities; 2. Apply ice; 3. Refer to a physician if symptoms and signs worsen or do not subside within a few days. **3 PTS**

MUSCULOSKELETAL INJURY SCENARIO 2

- *Injury:* Rib fracture. **2 PTS**
- *First aid steps:* 1. Rest from all activities; 2. If the athlete has breathing difficulties, an open chest wound, or a backward displaced (toward internal organs) rib, or the athlete is suffering from shock, call for emergency medical assistance; 3. If none of the above apply, send the athlete to a physician. **3 PTS**

MUSCULOSKELETAL INJURY SCENARIO 3

- *Injury:* Finger dislocation. **2 PTS**
- *First aid steps:* 1. Send for emergency medical assistance if the athlete is suffering from shock or there are signs of nerve damage or disrupted circulation; 2. If none of the above, immobilize the hand and finger in the position in which you found them; 3. Monitor and treat for shock as needed; 4. Apply ice; 5. Send to a physician. **3 PTS**

MUSCULOSKELETAL INJURY SCENARIO 4

- *Injury:* Hamstring strain. **2 PTS**
- *Severity:* Grade II—the key word is *moderate.* **1 PT**
- *First aid steps:* 1. Rest from all activities; 2. Monitor and treat for shock as needed and send for emergency medical assistance if it occurs; 3. Send for emergency medical assistance if the muscle is completely torn (rolled up); 4. Prevent the athlete from walking on the injured leg; 5. Apply ice to the injury and send the athlete to a physician (if emergency medical assistance is not sent for). **3 PTS**

MUSCULOSKELETAL INJURY SCENARIO 5

- *Injury:* Knee sprain. **2 PTS**
- *Severity:* Grade I. **I PT**
- *First aid steps:* 1. Rest the athlete from painful activities; 2. Apply ice; 3. Refer the athlete to a physician if symptoms and signs worsen or do not subside within a few days. **3 PTS**

MUSCULOSKELETAL INJURY SCENARIO 6

- *Injury:* Ankle sprain. **2 PTS**
- *Severity:* Grade II or III—either answer is acceptable for this scenario. **I PT**
- *First aid steps:* 1. Rest the athlete from all activities that require use of the leg; 2. Prevent the athlete from walking on the injured leg; 3. Monitor and treat for shock as needed and send for emergency medical assistance if it occurs; 4. Send for emergency medical assistance if any of the following are present: (a) signs of fracture—obvious deformity or pain at the site of the injury when tibia and fibula are gently squeezed above or below the injury, or pain along the midline of the lower third of the tibia or fibula; (b) symptoms and signs of nerve compression (tingling and numbness); (c) symptoms and signs of disrupted blood supply (bluish toes and toenails); 5. Apply ice to the injury and send the athlete to a physician (if emergency medical assistance is not sent for). **3 PTS**

TOTAL POINTS POSSIBLE: 34

Sport First Aid Wrap-Up

(16 minutes)

PURPOSE: To help you review what has been learned in the class and understand the process and procedures for completing the rest of the Sport First Aid course.

LEARNING OBJECTIVES

In this unit, you will learn

- answers to any of your remaining questions and
- the process and procedures for completing the rest of the Sport First Aid course.

Unit Overview

Topic	Activities	Time (minutes)
A. Unit Introduction	Hear about the unit's purpose, objectives, and agenda.	1
B. Sport First Aid Classroom Course Summary	Review the main topics covered in the course. Ask any remaining questions about first aid steps.	5
C. Next Steps	Test preparation Test procedures	5
D. Thanks and Good Luck!	Final questions and goodbyes	5

UNIT CONTENT

A Unit Introduction (I minute)

- Ask any remaining questions
- Your next steps for completing the Sport First Aid course.

B Sport First Aid Classroom Course Summary (5 minutes)

Today we have discussed

- your role on the athletic health care team,
- types of injuries and illnesses and how they occur,
- performing the emergency action steps and the Heimlich maneuver,
- conducting the physical assessment and providing immediate first aid,
- moving injured or sick athletes,
- head and spine injuries, and
- musculoskeletal injuries.

C Next Steps (5 minutes)

Test Preparation

1. Read all chapters in *Sport First Aid*, and read them **carefully**, because all of the test questions are based on content in the book.

2. Complete all units in the *Sport First Aid Online Component*. Your key code to access the online component is on the key code letter included in the Sport First Aid classroom test package. **While you're in the online component, please also complete the course evaluation** because your opinions are very important in helping to improve the course.

Testing

1. Review pages 1 and 2 of the Sport First Aid test instructions and determine whether you'll take the online test or the paper–pencil test.

2. Refer to page 72 in the workbook for the information you'll need to enter to start the test.

3. When you're ready to take the test, follow the instructions in the Sport First Aid test instructions:

   a. **If** you're taking the online test, follow the instructions in part B.

   b. **If** you're taking the paper–pencil test, follow the instructions in part C.

   c. You should plan to complete these two steps by _____.

   d. If you do not successfully pass your Sport First Aid test within one year of the last date of your course (today), you will have to take the entire course over again and pay all of the course fees again.

D Thanks and Good Luck! (5 minutes)

(Notes)

Test Information

Write the test information in the second column.

Required information	Write information below
Your ID number (from the course roster)	
Key code (on the top of page 1 of the Sport First Aid test instructions)	
Instructor's ID number	
Instructor's last name	
Organization code	
Last date of the course	
Course code (If you're taking the paper–pencil test, you'll need this code. The course code is located at the bottom right of the last page of the test. It begins with the letters BB followed by two numbers, for example, BB10, BB11, or BB12.)	
Date you need to complete the test by (If the instructor tells you a completion date, write it in the next column. Otherwise you should complete the test by one year from today's date; write that date in the next column.)	